As Time Goes By...

Exclusive Distributors:
Music Sales Limited
8/9 Frith Street,
London W1V 5TZ, England.
Music Sales Pty Limited
120 Rothschild Avenue,
Rosebery, NSW 2018,
Australia.

This book © Copyright 1992 by
Wise Publications
Order No.AM88875
ISBN 0.7119.2958.0

Designed by Pearce Marchbank Studios.
Compiled by Peter Evans & Pearce Marchbank.

Music Sales' complete catalogue lists thousands of titles
and is free from your local music shop, or direct from
Music Sales Limited. Please send a cheque/postal order
for £1.50 for postage to: Music Sales Limited,
Newmarket Road, Bury St. Edmunds, Suffolk IP33 3YB.

Your Guarantee of Quality:

As publishers, we strive to produce every book to the
highest commercial standards.
This book has been carefully designed to minimise awkward
page turns and to make playing from it a real pleasure.
Particular care has been given to specifying acid-free,
neutral-sized paper which has not been chlorine bleached
but produced with special regard for the environment.
Throughout, the printing and binding have been planned to
ensure a sturdy, attractive publication which should give
years of enjoyment.
If your copy fails to meet our high standards,
please inform us and we will gladly replace it.

Printed in the United Kingdom by
Dotesios Limited, Trowbridge, Wiltshire.

Wise Publications
London/New York/Sydney

Play them again Sam!

As Time Goes By

Words & Music by Herman Hupfeld.

must get down to earth, at times re - lax, re - lieve the ten - sion. No

mat - ter what the pro - gress, or what may yet be proved, The

sim - ple facts of life are such they can - not be re - moved.

You must re - mem - ber this, a kiss is still a kiss, A

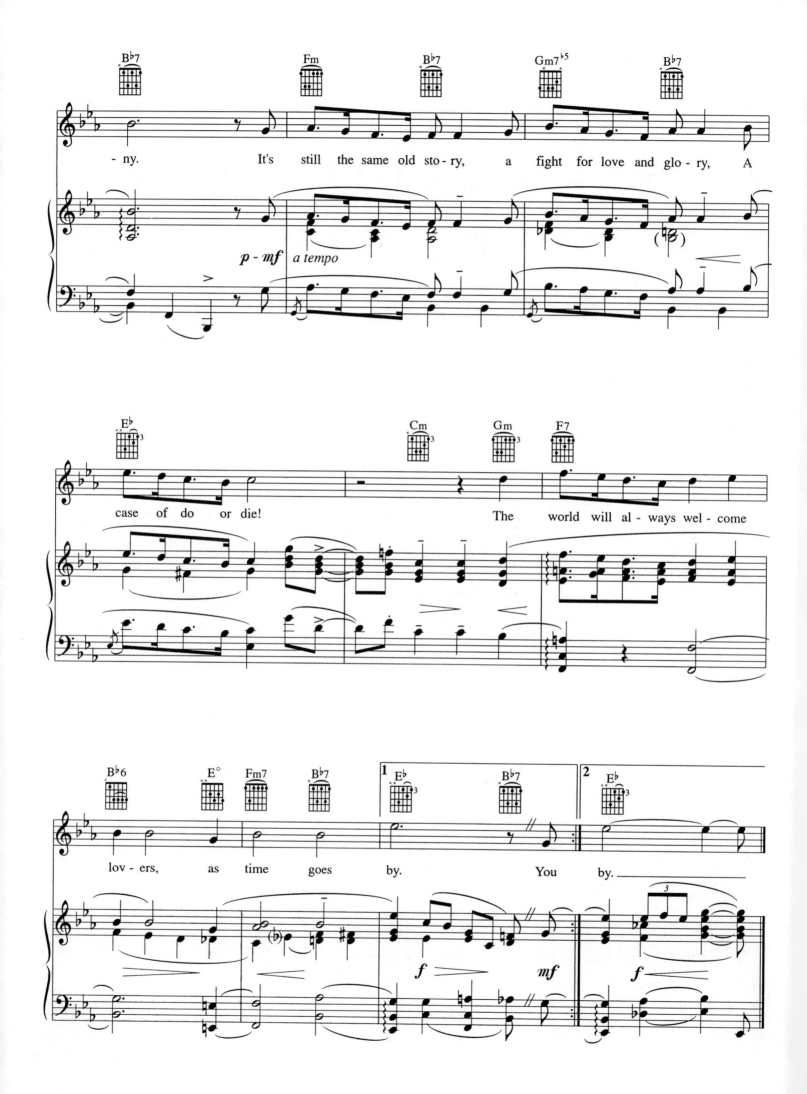

-ny.   It's   still   the same old sto-ry,   a   fight   for love and glo-ry,   A

case   of   do   or   die!   The   world   will al - ways wel - come

lov - ers,   as   time   goes   by.   You   by. _____

8

All The Things You Are

Music by Jerome Kern. Words by Oscar Hammerstein II.

Moderately, with expression

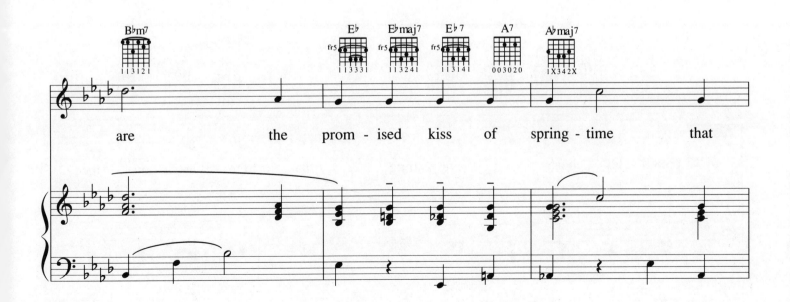

makes the lone - ly win - ter seem long. _____

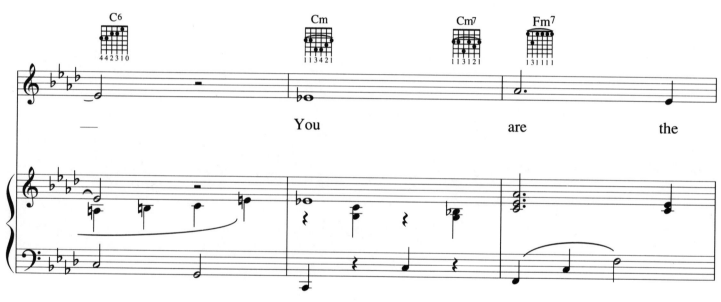

— You are the

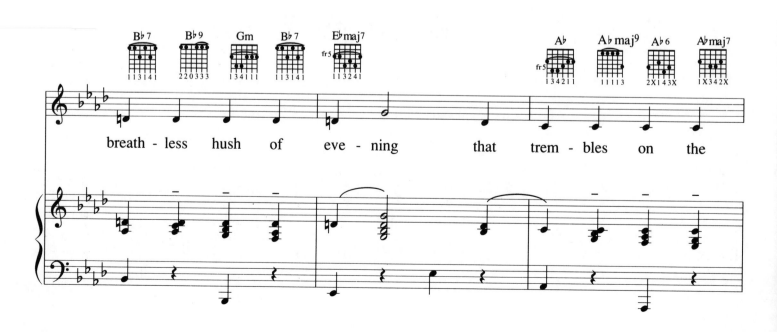

breath - less hush of eve - ning that trem - bles on the

brink of a love - ly song. _____ You are the

ang - el glow _____ that lights a star, _____

___ the dear - est things I know _____ are what you

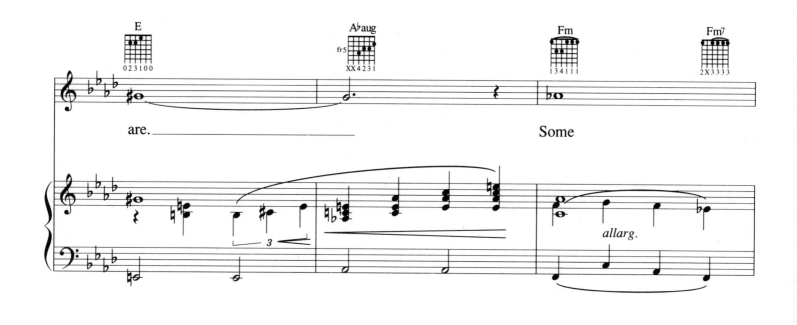

are._____ Some

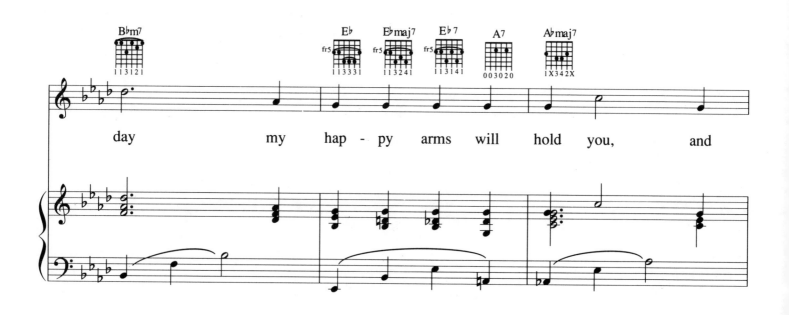

day my hap - py arms will hold you, and

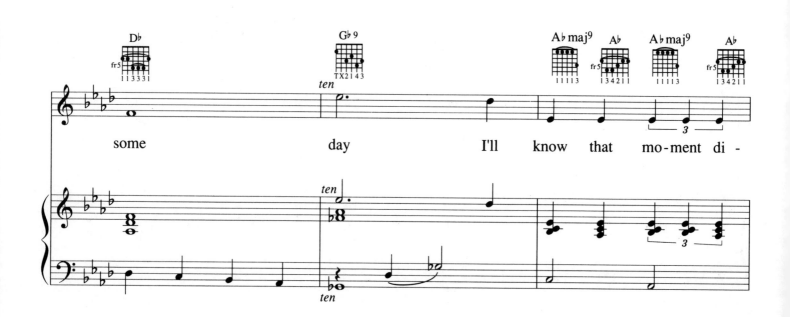

some day I'll know that mo - ment di -

vine,   when   all   the   things   you   are,   are

mine!   mine!

cresc.

sf   *molto rall.*

Always In My Heart

Words by Kim Gannon. Music by Ernesto Lecuona.

heart _____ and when skies a - bove are grey _____

____ I re - mem - ber that you care _____ and then and there the sun breaks

thru. _____ Just be - fore I go to sleep _____

____ there's a ren - dez - vous I keep _____ and the dream I al - ways

meet _____ helps me for-get we're far a-part. _____

I don't know ex-act-ly when dear _____ but I'm sure we'll meet a-

-gain dear _____ and my dar-ling till we do _____ you are al-ways in my

heart. You are al-ways in my heart. _____

Angel Eyes

Words by Earl Brent. Music by Matt Dennis.

Because Of You

Words & Music by Arthur Hammerstein & Dudley Wilkinson.

heart._____ Be - cause of you my ro - mance had its

start._____ Be - cause of you the sun will shine, the moon and

stars will say you're mine for - ev - er and nev - er to

part._____ I on - ly live for your love and your

Don't Blame Me

Words & Music by Jimmy McHugh & Dorothy Fields.

1. Ev-er since the luck-y night I found you___ I've hung a-round you,___ just like a
2. I like ev-'ry sin-gle thing a-bout you___ With-out a doubt you___ are like a

fool   Fall-ing head and heels in love like   a kid out   of
dream.   In my mind I find a   pic-ture   of us as   a

school

team.

My poor heart is in an aw-ful state now____ But it's too

Ev-er since the hour of our meet-ing____ I've been re-

late now____ to call a halt.

peat-ing____ a sil-ly phrase

So if I be-come a

Hop-ing that you'll un-der-

nui-sance it's all your fault!

stand me one of these days.

Don't blame

me for fall-ing in love with you I'm un-der your spell but

East Of The Sun
(And West Of The Moon)

Words & Music by Brooks Bowman.

you and I._____ East of the sun_____ and

west of the moon,_____ We'll build a dream-house__ of

love, dear. Near to the sun in the

day, Near to the moon at night, We'll

live in a love-ly way, dear, Liv-ing on love and pale moon-light.

Just you and I,_____ for ev-er and a day,_____

_____ Love will not die,_____ we'll

keep it that way,_____ Up a-mong the

stars we'll find A har-mo-ny of life to a love-ly tune,

East of the sun and west of the moon,

dear, East of the sun and west of the

moon. moon.

Ev'ry Time We Say Goodbye

Words & Music by Cole Porter.

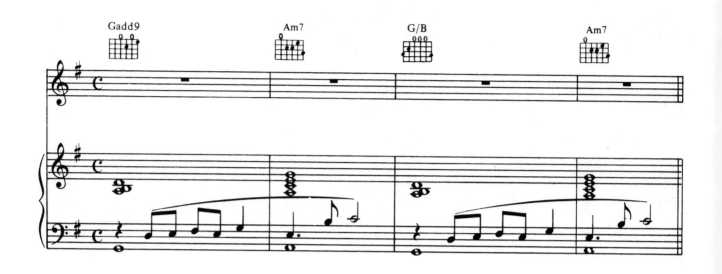

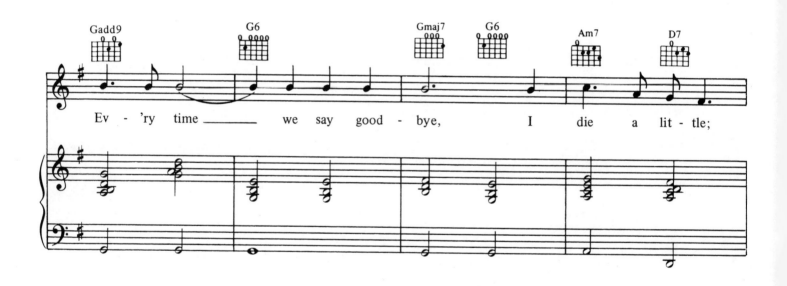

Ev - 'ry time _____ we say good - bye, I die a lit - tle;

ev - 'ry time _____ we say good - bye, I won - der why a lit - tle;

To Coda ⊕

34

we say good - bye.

Falling In Love Again

Music & Original Words by Friedrich Hollander.
English Words by Reg Connelly.

when I re-flect e - mo - tion there's no need to guess.

REFRAIN

I'm fall - ing in love a - gain, nev - er want - ed to,

p-f

what am I to do, I can't help it. Love's al - ways

been my game, play it how I may, I was made that way, I can't

Fools Rush In

Words by Johnny Mercer. Music by Rube Bloom.

where wise men nev-er go, _____ but wise men nev-er fall in love _____

so how are they to know? _____ When we met _____

I felt my life be-gin; _____ So o-pen up your heart, and let _____

this fool rush in. in. _____

I'll Never Smile Again, Until I Smile At You

Words & Music by Ruth Lowe.

- lize, That our ro - mance is through. _____ I'll nev - er love a - gain I'm so in love with you. _____ I'll nev - er thrill a - gain to some-bo - dy new _____

I'm Gettin' Sentimental Over You

Words by Ned Washington. Music by Geo. Bassman.

Lazy River

Words & Music by Hoagy Carmichael & Sidney Arodin.

I like la - zy wea - ther, I like la - zy days,

Can't be blamed for hav - ing la - zy ways, Some old la - zy riv - er

sleeps be - side my door, Whis - p'ring to the sun - lit shore.

CHORUS

Up a la - zy riv - er by the old mill - run, That la - zy, la - zy riv - er in the noon - day sun, Lin - ger in the shade of a kind old tree, Throw a - way your trou - bles, dream a dream with me. ____

Long Ago And Far Away

Music by Jerome Kern. Words by Ira Gershwin.

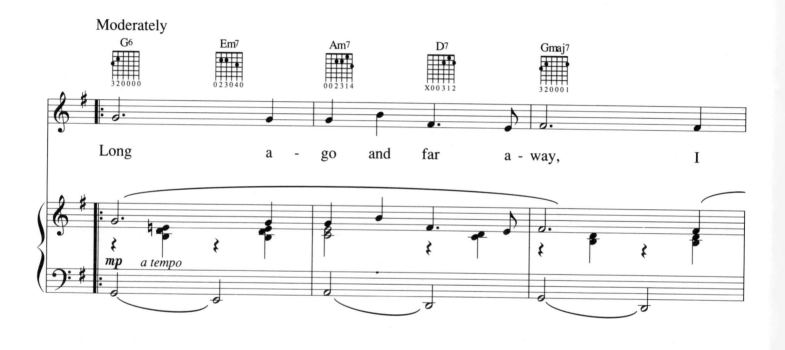

Long a - go and far a - way, I

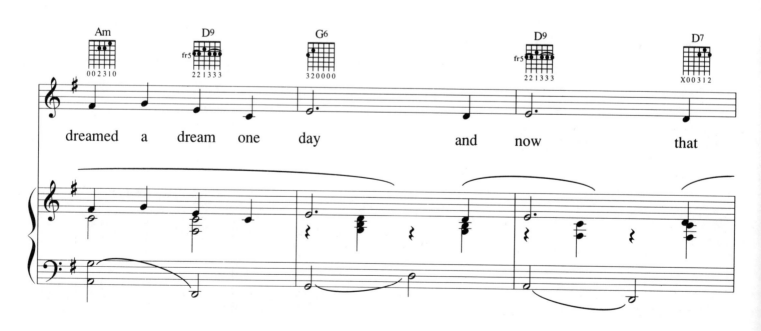

dreamed a dream one day and now that

Just one look and then I knew____ that all I longed for long a - go was for long a - go was

1. you.

2. you.____

P.S. I Love You

Words by Johnny Mercer. Music by Gordon Jenkins.

but all in all, I can't com-plain;

was it dust- y on the train? P. S. I love you.

Write to the Brown's just as soon as you're a - ble, they came a-round to

call.

I burned a hole in the din- ing room ta - ble,

Stars Fell On Alabama

Words by Mitchell Parish. Music by Frank Perkins.

dra - ma, we kissed in a field of white, and stars fell on Al - a -

ba - ma last night. I can't for-get the

glam - our, your eyes held a ten - der light, and stars fell on Al - a -

ba - ma last night. I nev-er planned in my im-a-gi-

na - tion ___ a sit - u - a - tion ___ so hea-ven - ly, ___ A fai-ry land where no one else could

en - ter, ___ and in the cen - tre ___ just you and me, dear. My heart beat like a

ham - mer, my arms wound a-round you tight, and stars fell on Al - a -

ba - ma last night.

night. ___

Stormy Weather

Words by Ted Koehler. Music by Harold Arlen.

There I've Said It Again

Words & Music by Redd Evans & Dave Mann.

The Last Time I Saw Paris

Music by Jerome Kern. Words by Oscar Hammerstein II.

Moderately

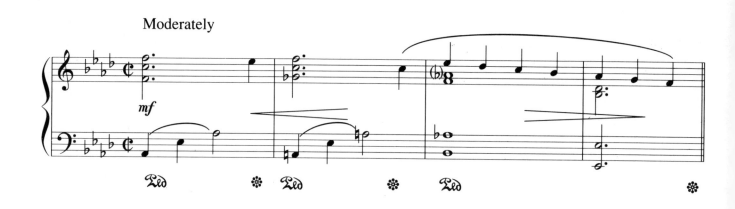

The last time I saw Par - is her heart was warm and

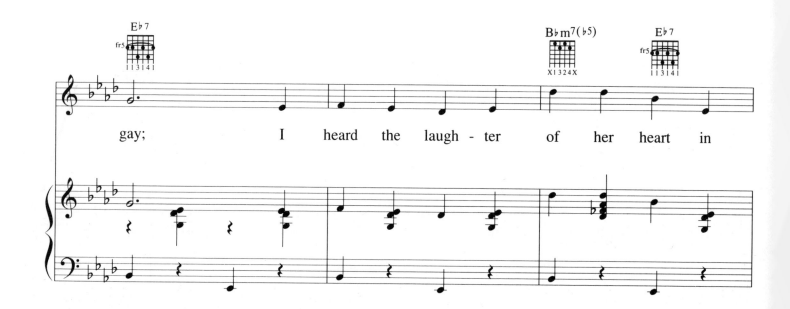

gay;   I heard the laugh - ter of her heart in

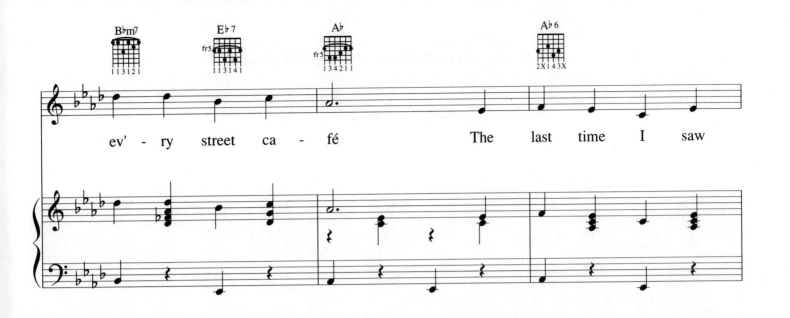

ev' - ry street ca - fé   The last time I saw

Par - is,   her trees were dressed for spring,   and

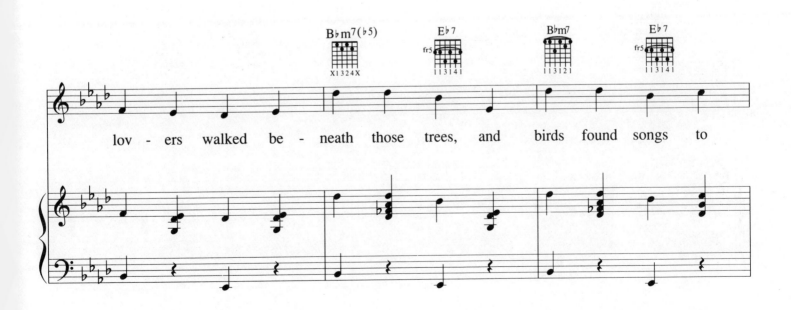

lov - ers walked be - neath those trees, and birds found songs to

sing.   I   dodged   the   same   old   tax - i   cabs   that

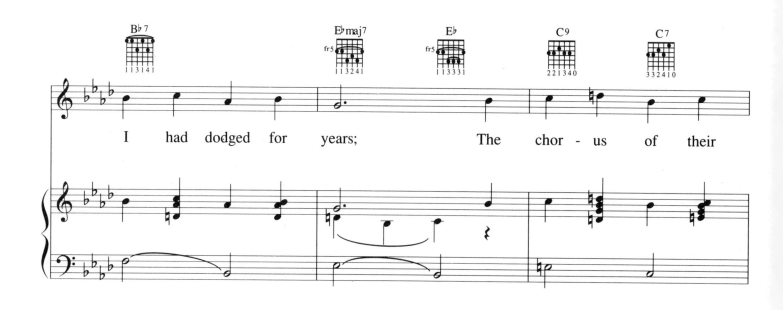

I   had   dodged   for   years;   The   chor - us   of   their

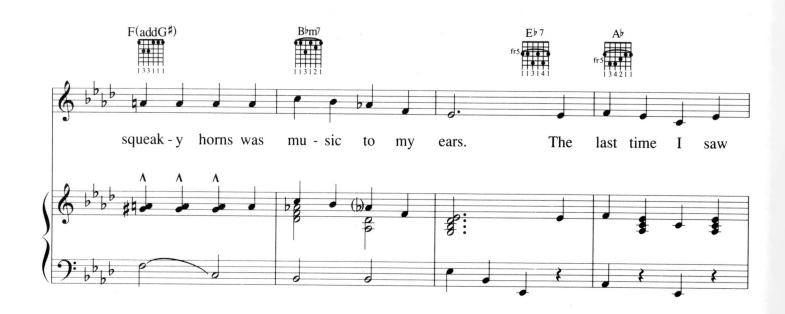

squeak - y horns was mu - sic to my ears.   The   last time I saw

The Night We Called It A Day

Words by Tom Adair. Music by Matt Dennis.

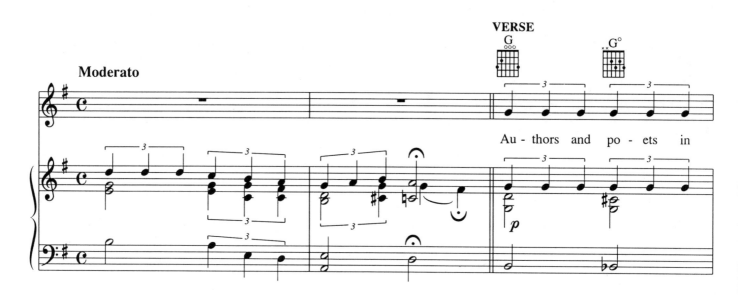

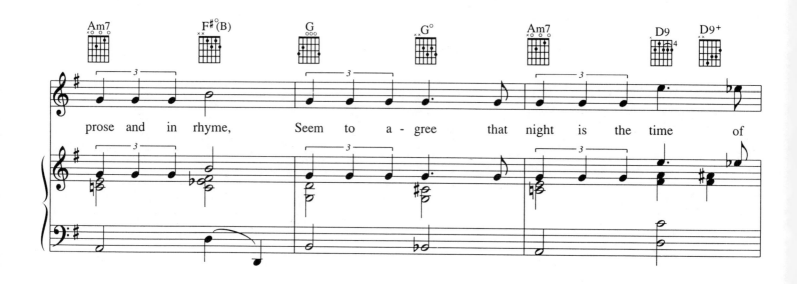

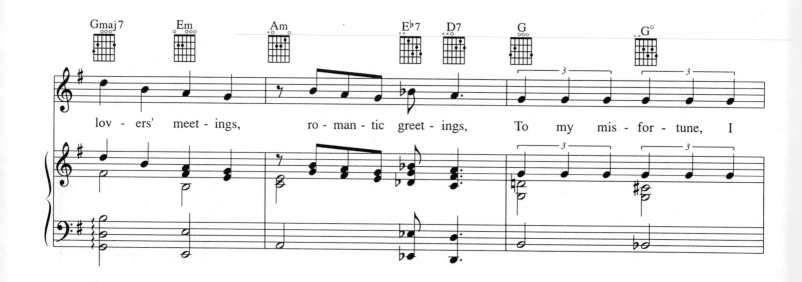

song, No blu - er was he than I, The moon went

down, stars were gone, But the sun did - n't rise with the

dawn, There was - n't a thing left to say, The

night we called it a day. There was a day.

The Very Thought Of You

Words & Music by Ray Noble.

For sleep-ing or wak-ing, dear,— I find;—
I'll on - ly be sat-is-fied— with you;—

poco rit.

REFRAIN

The ver - y thought of you,— And I for-get to do,—

p–mf

The lit -tle or - di-na - ry things that ev'-ry-one

ought to do.— I'm liv - ing in a kind of

day - dream, I'm hap - py as a king, And fool - ish tho' it

may seem, To me _____ that's ev' - ry - thing. _____ The mere i -

dea of you, _____ The long - ing here for you, _____

You'll nev - er know how slow the mo - ments go 'till I'm

Till The End Of Time

Words & Music by Buddy Kaye & Ted Mossman.

Slowly and very expressively

I wished up-on a star for some-one to share what each day would bring,

And you, my dar-ling, are that some-one Meant for me to cling to

Till Then

Words & Music by Guy Wood, Eddie Seller & Sol Marcus.

Try A Little Tenderness

Words & Music by Harry Woods, Jimmy Campbell & Reg Connelly.

woman loves a man, ___ He's a he - ro in her
worries drag you down, ___ It's so ea - sy to for -

eyes, ___ And a he - ro he can al - ways be, If
get. ___ But make the ef - fort all just the same, And

he'll just re - al - ize.
see the thrill you'll get.

CHORUS Tenderly

She may be wea - ry,

Wo - men do get wea - ry, Wear-ing the same shab - by dress,

And when she's wea-ry, Try a lit-tle ten-der-ness.

You know she's wait-ing, Just an-ti-ci-pat-ing, Things she may nev-er poss-

ess. While she's with-out them, Try a lit-tle ten-der-ness.

It's not just sen-ti-men-tal,_____ She

Violets For Your Furs

Words by Tom Adair. Music by Matt Dennis.

Will You Still Be Mine?

Words by Tom Adair. Music by Matt Dennis.